The Complete Book of
MAKE UP

Sarah Collins

Designed by
Philip Clucas MSIAD

Photography by
Peter Barry

Produced by
Ted Smart and
David Gibbon

BOOK CLUB ASSOCIATES
LONDON

Contents

Introduction

It is not an overstatement to say that every woman has her own kind of beauty. It is, however, very true to say that there are many who are unsure about how to make the best of that natural beauty and don't know about the enormous psychological boost that making the most of yourself gives you.

With some, it's a natural shyness – a feeling that wearing make-up would make them seem different from their normal selves. For others, it's more a question of not really knowing how to use cosmetics in the right way that leads them to ignore the make-up counters in the stores. Yet the art of making up is not to change but to create illusions; to enhance, to disguise and it is very simple and easy to learn.

In the pages of this book there are make-ups for everyone. We have set out to show you just some of the thousands of different ways that make-up can be made to work for you. Some of the ideas may shock, some may even seem a little dull, but they are there to show you graphically some of the magic to encourage you to be more adventurous, to get you out of a rut or just to give you some new ideas to try out.

3

Above *Sally has a classically pretty face – good shape, high cheekbones, almond shaped eyes that are not too big and certainly not too small, a straight unprominent nose and full lips. We purposely left her hair slicked back and away from her face so that the real dramatic effects created by make-up are shown even more graphically.*

1: *Sleek and elegant with muted shades.*

2: *Clashing colours used to stunning effect.*

3: *Disco glitter and colour.*

2

1

Tough, strong and theatrical.

Cats eyes sensation.

Clashing oranges and blues can go together.

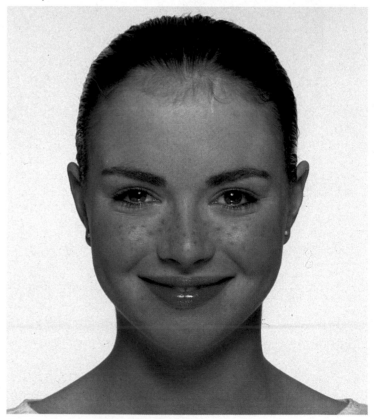

Fresh and pretty with fake freckles.

Cover girl glamour.

Outdoor fresh and natural.

Elegant sixties shape and shade.

Sculptured and sensational.

Chapter 1
The Bare Canvas

Just as a beautiful painting starts life on a clean fresh canvas, so too a good make-up starts from a clear, clean complexion. Of course it's a rare person that has a completely trouble-free skin but problems can be minimised by following the time-worn ritual of cleanse, tone and moisturise night and morning and always before applying make-up.

Learn to recognise your skin type, it's either dry, greasy or a combination of the two with a greasy panel down the centre of the face. Select skincare products to suit and religiously use them. Get plenty of fresh air; eat as many fresh fruits and green vegetables as you can and avoid fried foods, to aid a healthy clear complexion.

Facial Movement

Treat the skin on your face gently, don't ever tug or pull it, it's very delicate and you'll only encourage wrinkles or broken veins. Use only fingertips to massage and follow these movements whether applying makeup, cleansing, toning or moisturising.

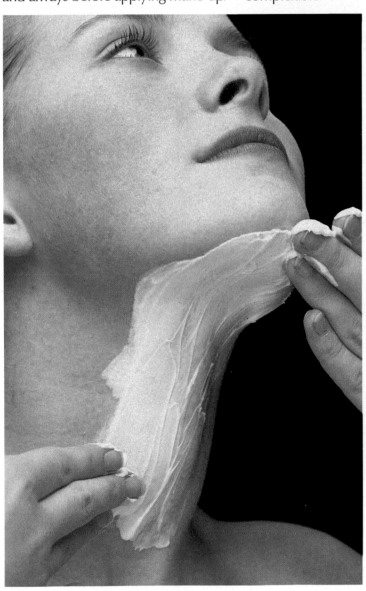

1: *Upward, sweeping movements from the collar bone up the neck.*

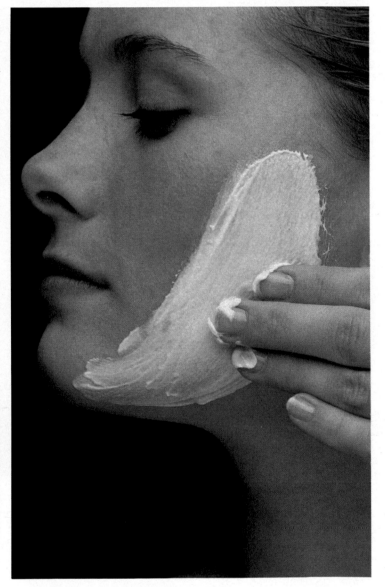

2: *Upward and outward from the chin to the temples.*

3: *Stroking, gentle movements down the centre of the nose.*

needs medical treatment. (Skin with clinical acne tends to look very bumpy, red, and often has a certain amount of scaling too – very different from a normal teenage spotty skin.) Sadly, doctors have not yet found the complete answer to acne and the treatments are many and various. On a happier note, in most cases, acne does decrease with age and often goes completely by mid-teens.

Wrinkles Well, they come to us all in time, but a good skincare routine can help a great deal to keep them at bay. Wrinkles start to happen as your skin loses its natural elasticity anytime from the age of thirty onwards. Keep them under control by moisturising and watching for some of the danger signs: dryness; frowning; pulling the skin; too much sun.

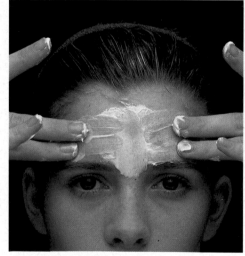

4: *From centre ot forehead upwards and out along the forehead.*

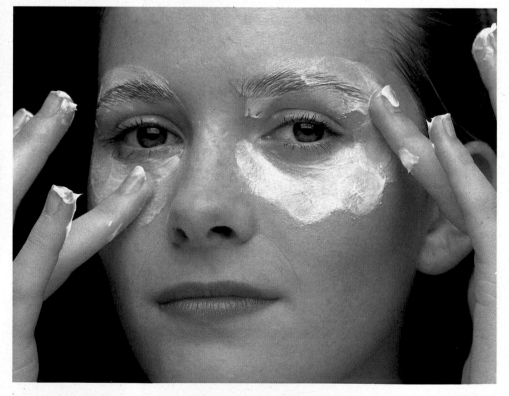

5: *Gentle circular movements around the eyes.*

Spotting Trouble

Spots It's a pretty rare person who doesn't get the odd spot and they are very annoying, but not always impossible to deal with. Keep your skin as clean as possible and apply the type of spot cream or lotion that contains benzoyl peroxide to dry it out quickly. Never squeeze a spot because the bacteria that cause the spot can spread and encourage another eruption elsewhere on the face. Providing you

have treated the spot with cream, then you can safely cover it with make-up to disguise.

Clinical Acne This can be a very real problem for some, especially young teenagers. This should not be confused with normal teenage spots as it usually

Broken Veins Fair complexions of soft, fine skin are particularly prone to suffering from broken veins – tiny little red lines that occur on the side of the nose and cheeks. They are caused by

A face mask will leave your skin clear and refreshed: refining pores and removing wrinkles.

various outside influences namely a) no protection from excessive sun and wind. b) too much alcohol. c) rough treatment like squeezing, pulling and tugging of the skin. As it's practically impossible to rid yourself of them once they've appeared prevention is a much better idea. Therefore, avoid their occurrence by protecting your face with moisturiser and foundation if you live a healthy outdoor life. Avoid drinking to excess and even eating too much spicey food and treat your face gently.

Blackheads Blackheads and greasy skin tend to go hand in hand. They are caused by the pores becoming blocked with the skin's natural lubricant, sebum. The characteristic black spot that gives them their name is the sebum oxidising in the air, not dirt as is commonly thought. To prevent their occurrence, every time you cleanse simply massage more carefully around the greasy panels and take care to clear the pores with skin tonic when you've finished.

Use this method to prevent and dislodge blackheads that have already formed. A once a week face mask also helps a great deal. But, please, never squeeze a blackhead.

Whiteheads These tend to form around the eyes. They look exactly like blackheads, but, because they are under the skin, the black spot never forms. They are caused by sebum too, but it has become blocked under the skin. One of the reasons that they form is cleansing with the wrong product and heavy oil used to remove make-up is often blamed for them. You cannot remove them yourself and the best method is to go to a beauty salon for an electrolysis treatment.

Avoid the occurrence of whiteheads by using only specialised eye make-up remover, cleansing cream or lotion.

Enlarged Pores This problem is often known as 'orange peel skin' because that's exactly what it looks like – the outer skin of an orange. This happens most commonly on greasy skin and really there is very little that can be done about it except regular toning and having a weekly face mask to help refine the pores.

Superfluous Hair Dark haired people often suffer this problem. We all have hair covering our faces but sometimes it just happens to show more. If your particular problem is fine, dark hair on the upper lip then regular treatment with a facial bleach is a good idea. Thicker, dark hair on cheeks and upper lips can be more of a problem though and there are three possible courses of action 1) Bleaching. 2) Depilation, use a mild facial depilatory once every three weeks or so. 3) Permanent removal with a course of electrolysis. If you choose the first two methods, patch test a small area of skin on the inside of your arm first to make sure that you don't have an allergic reaction. If you select the final course of action, make sure that you go to a beauty therapist who is a registered electrolysis practitioner and ask how long the treatment is liable to take as this can be pretty costly.

Allergies It's not at all uncommon for us all at some time or another to suffer an allergic reaction to the products that we

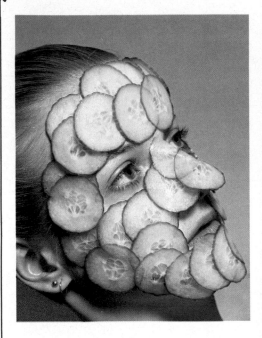

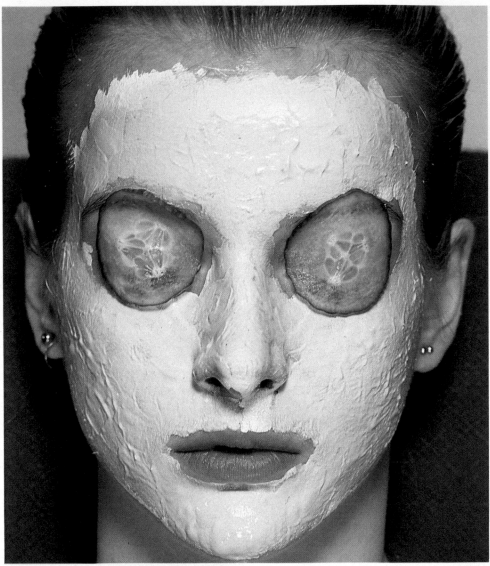

use and this can manifest itself in many different ways. Tiny red spots that itch, a burning rash and swelling are all sure signs of an allergy. Often it's nothing to do with the make-up you're using but more likely to be caused by something you ate, a form of hay fever, nerves or even a new perfume you're wearing. But if you do get an allergy, it's best to watch your cleansing and make-up routine by switching to hypo-allergenic and perfume free products until it has abated.

Home Beauty Treatments

Even the most trouble free of complexions needs an occasional lift to help revitalise and rejuvenate. And, one of the quickest and most effective ways of doing this is to treat yourself to a face mask. This will help refine pores, iron out tiny wrinkles and leave your skin clear and refreshed.

If you go to a beauty salon for a professional facial a major part of the treatment will involve rest and relaxation. Therefore, before embarking on an at-home facial it's a must to make sure that, for at least fifteen minutes, you are free from interruption. Lock the door and take the phone off the hook. Run a warm bath, cleanse your face thoroughly and while you're freshly bathed and wrapped in a warm towel put on your chosen mask. Set your alarm to ring in ten

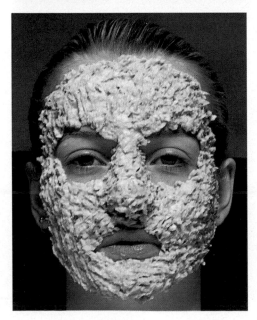

minutes and lie back and relax with cotton wool pads wrung out in cold water, or cucumber slices, over your eyes. When your time is up, thoroughly rinse off all traces of the mask and splash your face with cool water to tone.

There is an enormous variety of branded face masks to choose from, suited to all skin types but your larder too contains the makings for your own home-made kind that can work just as efficiently. Cucumber is wonderful for skin. Simply cover your face with slices and let the oil soak in. Sliced or pulped strawberries are beautiful too if a little costly. But for a highly effective quick lift, there's nothing better than the skin of a fresh pineapple – the inside juicy part of course. Pineapple, apart from being

really best to stick to unperfumed facial soap and once a week gently slough away dead skin by using a man's clean shaving brush or special cosmetic brush. Remember always though that soap must be thoroughly rinsed away as a residue on the skin can cause excessive dryness and itching.

Sparkling Eyes

Because they are the visible, living part of you, care of your eyes is very important indeed. Of course it goes without saying that sleep is one of the best beauty treatments not only for your eyes but your whole body too – eight hours a

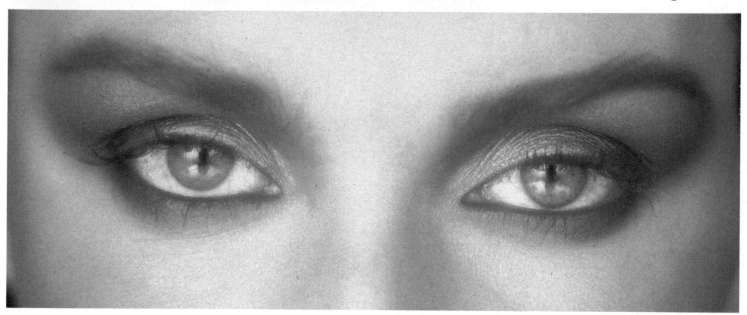

Sparkling healthy eyes are perhaps the greatest aid to beauty, so care for them well.

delicious to eat is packed full of living enzymes that are said to work miracles on tired skin.

If you've been making fresh mayonnaise, don't throw away the egg white. Instead, whisk it up and pat it gently onto the face, leave for ten minutes and rinse off with cold water – a lovely pick-me-up.

It's a pretty sobering fact that the only living part of the human body that is visible is the eyes. The rest is in fact dead, as the living skin is under a fine layer of

dead cells that are constantly being lost and replaced from below. Normal cleansing and washing helps to peel the old dead skin away but sometimes a little encouragement is needed to avoid clogging pores and the characteristic sallowness of tired skin. This is known as exfoliation. Face masks do this job very well but oily skins can also benefit from a once a week wash with a granular cleanser. This type of cleanser is usually called a 'facial scrub' and contains tiny granules. In fact, fine ground oatmeal mixed to a paste with water and gently massaged in circular movements is also an extremely efficient exfoliator.

If you're a soap and water addict it's

night is the ideal but not always possible. But continual late nights will soon start to show, with tiny strain lines and perhaps puffiness all around your eyes.

The area around your eyes is the most delicate on the body so the 'no tugging or pulling' rule is even more important here. A useful tip is only to use your little finger to apply make-up or creams to avoid exerting too much pressure on this area. Keep face masks, exfoliating aids and heavy creams away from your eyes too. If you are starting to get fine lines and wrinkles, gently massage in a special eye cream nightly, try to relax as much as possible and have your eyes tested; you may need glasses.

Chapter 2

The Basics

The old saying 'a workman is only as good as his tools' is very true of the difference between being professional about your make-up or just plain amateur. Don't be frightened by our picture of the contents of a professional make-up kit; I just wanted to show you the infinite variety of kinds of cosmetics and aids that are available. But this should at the same time give you some idea of

Just a small portion of a professional make-up kit to show the infinite variety of cosmetics that are on the market including products from: Revlon, Maybelline, Max Factor, Boots, Cover Girl Lancôme, Helena Rubenstein and Miners.

the variety of cosmetics and tools needed to create the myriad different looks and styles that you can see in the pages of this book.

Although most cosmetics manufacturers supply brushes and applicators with their products, there is really no substitute for some of the more professional ones that make making-up a much simpler process. Also, the many

different formulations of products suit different techniques and lifestyles. Learn these techniques and learn how to apply the products successfully and making-up is going to be so much easier to do.

Starting Right

Here's a list of the basic items that you will need before starting work:–

1. **Tissues** – For cleansing and correcting mistakes, nothing else will do.

2. **Cotton Buds** – Invaluable for mopping-up eye and lip make-up mistakes.

3. **Cotton Wool** – For using damp to remove cleanser from the skin and to apply toner before moisturising.

4. **Brushes and applicators** – You need at least five. Choose a big fat one for blushing and shaping; two are needed for eyes, one shaped and one soft and fat for all over shading, a sponge tip applicator is very useful for applying pressed powder and cream shadows too; a lip brush is a must especially for outlining and smoother and longer lasting application.

5. **Cosmetic Sponge**– For even application of foundation, there is no substitute.

Make sure that everything that touches your face is clean and never use the first three items more than once, they're disposable so dispose of them the minute they've been used. Wash your brushes and applicators at least once a week in mild soapy water, rinse very well, gently pull them back into shape and let them dry overnight.

Your Cosmetic Kit

Are you one of those ladies who are putty in the hands of a good cosmetic sales lady? If you are then you probably have a drawer-full of products that you have either no idea how to use or no wish to use in the first place. I'm a great believer in having a whole wardrobe of

make-up on hand to cover every eventuality. But, for normal everyday wear there are really only a few items that you really do need to see you through. Open up your drawer and select items from this list because this is really all you need.

1. **Foundation** – Cake and cream foundations are best suited to dry or problem (spotty) skins; the mat cream types often called 'complete make-up suit combination and oily skin types. If your skin is normal, the cream type suits well.

2. **Cover Stick** – To hide dark shadows, spots and mild blemishes, cover sticks

are invaluable. Although they are formulated to cover spots they work wonders on disguising all manner of problems.

3. **Translucent Powder** – A must for setting your foundation, it's lighter and more controllable than pressed powder.

4. **Blusher** – Choose the type that suits your chosen foundation – creams are best used on top of cream and cake foundations and powders work well on 'complete' foundations.

5. **Shadows** – Whatever shape your eyes you're going to need at least three different shades to create the right kind of effect.

6. **Kohl Pencil** – Very useful for defining shape and even using in place of eye shadow for a quick make-up.

7. **Mascara** – Probably the most important cosmetic of all to enhance the natural beauty of your eyes.

8. Eyebrow Pencil & Tweezers – Use your tweezers to pluck stray hairs and neaten the shape, and a pencil to emphasise.

9. Lipstick – You'll need at least three different shades to suit every mood, occasion and outfit.

The Technique

The great art in making-up is to do it so well that it will last all day without constant re-touching. With all the various forms that cosmetics take and the many different formulations it is often a case of trial and error to choose a brand that really suits you. It is also a case of learning how to apply the different formulations in the correct way to make them last.

The Base

If you are one of those lucky few who are blessed with a perfect skin with even colouring then you will not need to use a foundation – just moisturise and carry on to the next stage of making up. If, on the other hand, you are like the majority of the population, your skin tones will need evening-up to make the perfect base. Choose your shade very carefully. Make use of the manufacturers' testers and apply a little to the back of your hand and check it in daylight. Ideally, the colour should exactly match your skin tones; failing that, choose a shade slightly darker but never lighter. Very dark skinned people often have trouble finding a foundation that's the right shade, in which case you should mix your own by blending two matching foundations together to achieve the right tones. The best way of doing this is to buy the same type and brand of products and mix them in an empty container (it's just like mixing paint).

Always apply foundation sparingly to avoid looking caked. Dot all over the face and neck and blend with a slightly dampened cosmetic sponge, remembering to use upward movements. When it's completely even, very gently finish off using downward movements so that the hairs on your face lie flat.

Covering Up Use your cover stick to

camouflage blemishes, and shadows under your eyes. Choose a shade lighter than your foundation and apply to the area to be hidden with your fingertip and blend with a clean brush.

Powdering Up To help set your foundation and provide a grease-free base for make-up, powder is a must and translucent powder is the easiest and most effective form to buy. Apply using a clean cotton wool ball and press gently onto the skin; when your face is covered, dust off the excess with the clean side of the cotton wool using downward movements to keep the hairs lying flat.

Blushing There are essentially three forms of blusher: gel, cream and powder.

If you prefer to use either gel or cream this should be applied before powdering. Simply dot the area to be shaded and blend carefully with fingertips. For powder blusher use a nice fat brush for even blending after powdering.

Make your blusher work for you to enhance your face shape – it's not there to add colour – it's there to create an illusion. The first rule to remember is that of light and shade. Use lighter shades (highlighters) to enhance your best features like cheekbones and darker shades to give the impression of depth and to hide.

The shades of blusher that you should choose really depend on your natural colouring. If for instance you have very olive skin, bright pinks just won't suit at all and shades of brown would look pretty wrong on a peaches and cream complexion. Ideally, too, the colour should never clash with your chosen outfit.

I have mentioned highlighters in this section because they are useful for helping to enhance your good natural features. Often, rather than buying a separate highlighter, powder eye shadow works just as well providing you choose pale peach, ivory or gold (this looks wonderful with a tan).

Remember that your face is rounded with no angular lines so always blend blusher and highlighter well and never colour in straight lines, to keep the look as natural as possible.

Eye Shadow There are pressed powders, creams, loose powders, cream and powder mixed, and pencils for you to choose from and there is a different technique for applying each one.

The most popular form of eye shadow is pressed powder; there's a huge colour variety to choose from and they really are the easiest to apply and have good lasting ability. Use either a brush or sponge tip applicator for best results.

Cream shadows are very suited to those with dry skin and should be applied with a sponge applicator.

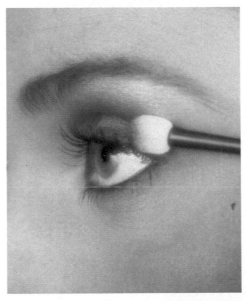

You literally draw the outline you need and then soften and blend using a stubby eyeshadow brush. A light dusting of translucent powder on top will help to maintain lasting ability.

Ideally, your pencils should have quite a good point and, because they are so soft, it's easy to break them when sharpening. To overcome this simply put your pencil in the refrigerator for about twenty minutes before sharpening and allow it to warm up again before applying to lids. This tip is also useful for sharpening kohl pencils.

When choosing colours you will need three basic shades, all complementing each other – a pale frosted shade for highlighting, a deep shade for shaping

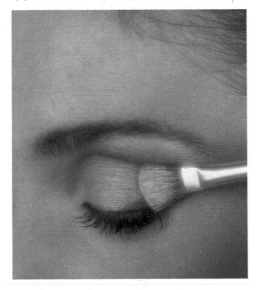

Loose powder shadows usually offer the brightest colours but can be tricky to apply. If using straight from the pot, a sponge applicator helps even application but, mixed with a little water on the back of the hand and applied with a brush, I find that they last longer.

Powder and cream mixes come with their own applicator. This form of eye shadow is probably the most durable and is very often waterproof too. They are very fast drying so blend with your fingertip straight after application.

Pencils Soft, eye pencils can produce some very interesting effects. Because they are soft and slightly greasy, they are best suited to dry and combination skins.

and avoid clogging on upper lashes – look upward for lower lashes. Brush on the lashes finely with separate coats for a soft, natural look.

Kohl Pencil The softest and easiest kind of eyeliner to use, kohl (sometimes known as kajal) pencils are perfect for defining eye shape and as a quick substitute for eye shadow. Using light movements, you draw a line and then blend with a brush to give a natural, soft shape.

Brow Shaping Your eyes need a frame to balance and your brows are that natural frame. Take care when plucking to let them keep their natural shape. Use a pencil to measure for perfect shape brows:– 1. Hold pencil vertical on line with the inner corner of your eye – your brow should stop at this line. 2. Hold

and a medium shade to add dimension. The colour range that you choose is very important too. For a beginners kit, you can't go far wrong with shades of beige, brown and copper – these suit practically all eye and fashion colours as they are fairly neutral. Don't believe the old adage that blues suit blue eyes and browns hazel and brown eyes: it's just not true.

Mascara All eyelashes need accentuating with mascara even if they are dark and thick. Choose a shade close to your own lash colour (blondes should never wear black) and apply carefully. Hold your mirror so that you look down into it and zigzag the brush to separate

pencil by your nostril diagonally across to the outer corner of your eye – the brow line should end here.

Brows always look best natural rather than over plucked. Using a baby's toothbrush or brow-brush, shape and tweeze only stray hairs that spoil the natural outline – gently hold the skin taut between fore and middle fingers and pluck outwards with the natural hair growth.

Always use a sharp brow pencil and draw small feathery strokes that look just like real hair.

Lipstick Once upon a time, this was woman's 'only' cosmetic. Now lipstick is there to complete the whole facial picture with soft, muted colours and gloss to make you look natural, and clear, bright colours to turn you into an instant glamour picture.

It's wise to choose three shades to complement your mood and outfit and, here again, beware of choosing clashing colours. For instance, orange lips and purple or blue eyes just don't work – soft, bluey pinks suit much better. Similarly, true pink lips just don't match soft brown eye shades.

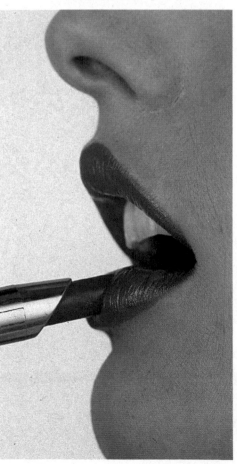

Let your lipstick match your mood.

Chapter 3

So who's got Problems?

There's practically no woman on this earth who is the perfect beauty; life just isn't like that. The stunning models who stare out at you from the pages of the magazines, the glorious stars who waft across the movie screens and even your best friend who always manages to look that bit more beautiful than you, all probably have their problems – they're just well disguised, that's all!

In the pages of this book you'll see, in some of the step-by-step pictures, spots being hidden, dark shadows being painted out and all manner of tricks that can be used to camouflage. Yet in the final picture, you'll notice that there's not a trace of a flaw. This isn't a result of special lighting techniques, it's just clever make-up. No matter what your particular problem may be, there are ways of hiding it without changing yourself drastically in any way. This is important to remember because, no matter what your make-up does for you, it should always mirror you and your personality and never try to turn you into something you are not.

Before starting work you will need to be totally honest with yourself. Place your mirror in a good natural light – it should always be there to ensure a perfect make-up – pull your hair away from your un-made-up face and take a good look. Yours' may be beautiful eyes or a perfect shape nose. Now look for the flaws like scars, blemishes, pointed nose, small eyes. All that you need to do now is learn to enhance your good points and disguise your bad – simple when you know how.

Spots and Blemishes In theory spots should be allowed to dry out naturally but nowadays certain preparations will work on this with or without foundation on top. As has been mentioned before, choose a cream or lotion containing Benzoyl Peroxide – your chemist will point you in the right direction – apply a little directly onto the spot, smooth in and allow to dry completely and then apply foundation all over. Minor spots will be hidden by just this but those awful, once-a month kind still tend to show through. Hide them by simply dabbing on the area with a cover stick in a shade paler than your foundation. Now, using a clean brush, blend the colour into the surrounding area.

Acne Most acne sufferers use special medicated products prescribed by a doctor to help with the problem. It's therefore a good idea to check with him whether make-up will affect the treatment in any way. If you get the go-ahead to wear make-up then you'll find a great ally in green cover cream. This is just like it sounds: it's the colour green and is perfect for blotting out the red colour that is so often associated with acne. Apply over the effected area with a clean sponge before covering with a light foundation. Don't be tempted to use a cake or stick foundation as this will tend to clog on the uneven parts of the skin and show up the imperfections all the more. Any red marks that can still be seen can then be covered by using the same method described in the Spots and Blemishes section.

High Colouring and Broken Veins It's so easy to disguise high colouring that it almost doesn't merit a mention here. But fine, pale skins do tend to have the problem of getting a little rosy especially when hot, and many do find it very embarrassing. Fine skin is also prone to broken veins especially on the cheek area. Therefore, anyone who has this type of complexion should pay a great deal of attention to protection with moisturiser and foundation, as exposure to harsh weather is often the principal cause of broken veins. Both problems, however, are quickly and simply hidden with the useful green cover cream applied under your normal make-up.

Wrinkles Laughter lines, frown lines, crow's feet, call them what you will, they come to us all in the end but they can be kept at bay by following a good skin care regime. It's now also generally felt that too much sun can be ageing so it's wise to take care when tanning to give your face extra protection too.

To diminish lines that are already there, you simply use a cover stick a shade lighter than your normal foundation colour. With a fine brush you paint along the wrinkle line then, using feathery strokes blend into the surrounding area.

Dark Shadows & Baggy Eyes Both these problems are often a sure sign of insufficient sleep. However, there are quite a few women who always suffer from one or the other no matter how many hours sleep they get. Here again, a light coloured cover stick or cake foundation, painted over the area and blended, will fade away dark shadows. Bags under the eyes can be diminished by painting or blending a slightly deeper shade of foundation over the area. A shading or dark brown kohl pencil under the lid also adds to the disguise.

Face Shaping It is said that the perfect face is heart shaped with forehead and cheekbones the same width, tapering to a well proportioned chin. In addition to this there are three other basic shapes – oval, round and square and we all fall into one of these categories. Each individual shape needs shading and highlighting in a different way to improve the proportions.

The rule of light to enhance and shade to diminish is used to best effect in basic face shaping. Therefore use a deep toned blusher to disguise a prominent chin or nose as well as to improve the

face shape. If you're blessed with good basic bone structure, use a highlighter to bring it out even more. Use a face shaping brush to apply highlighter – it's like a blusher brush but with slightly shorter, more stubby bristles. If you are using a cream highlighter, apply and blend with fingertips. Pay very special attention to avoid harsh unblended lines and follow the natural curving contours of your face.

2

3

4

1: Heart Shape *This is a very simple face to shape. Look in your mirror and grin. Your face will make a natural indentation just below your cheek bone and this where you should apply your blusher. Gently find your cheekbones with fingertips and apply your highlighter along this line, brushing or smoothing with your fingertips to blend naturally with your blusher.*

2: Oval Shape *You will need to create a false shape by shading over the cheek area and taking your blusher right up to your temples to give a slimmer effect. Here too, blend highlighter upwards and outwards along the line of your cheek bone.*

3: Round Shape *If your face is very rounded you need to give it a slimmed*

down effect. For the best effect you need two shades of blusher in the same colour tones. Use the lighter of the two shades first over the cheek area right down to your jaw line but fading away before reaching the temples. Blend the deeper shade around the edge of your face and into the centre of the cheek area. Highlight your cheek bone only until you are on line with the outer corners of your eyes. You can diminish a double chin by hiding with the lighter of your two blushers too.

4: Square Shape *Soften the angular line of your face by applying blusher in the centre of the cheek area and blending highlighter on the edge of your face. A little blusher on each side of the forehead will also give more shape and dimension.*

1

Girls With Glasses

Making-up for wearing glasses can be a little tricky, especially if you're very short sighted. Difficult it may be but impossible it certainly is not. Here, more than ever you really do need a good light and you need a large, magnifying mirror too. Keep your glasses to hand and, after finishing each stage,

pop them on and check out how you are doing in a normal mirror. Because they are going to be slightly hidden behind glass, you will need to emphasise your eyes even more to show them to best effect. Choose eye shades that complement the colour of your frames and follow the frame shape when shading – our photos here show you the importance of this.

Contact Lenses

Many people who wear contact lenses tend to have some difficulty in using eye make-up. Often eyes become sensitive and great care must be taken not to let any foreign bodies drop into the eyes.

It's a good idea to cut down the risk of sensitivity by selecting eye make-up that is hypo-allergenic and thus less likely to

1: *Pretty girl, pretty frames but, wearing the minimum of eye make-up does look rather plain and dull.*

2: *Notice the difference. Now, with blending tones of burgundy, pink and brown, her eyes look really stunning; really singing out from behind the glasses.*

cause irritation. If you have soft lenses, put them in before making-up but, if you wear hard lenses, insert them after you've

finished. Take care when removing your make-up too, tissues or dampened cotton wool are essential for this in order to avoid stray fibres getting in the eye.

It's best to stick to using cream, pressed powder or automatic eye shadow for shading but if you prefer to use loose powder mix it with water before brushing onto lids. Fibreless mascara and the softest of pencils are a must too and, anyone wearing contact lenses should avoid pencilling on the insides of lids.

Lip Service

No beautiful face is complete without lipstick and, as with all make-up techniques, there are rights and wrongs about the colours you choose as well as the application. As far as colour is concerned, it should never clash with your chosen outfit and should blend well with your chosen eye shadow shades. For the best and most long-lasting application, apply with a brush, blot with a tissue and re-apply. A light dusting with translucent powder before putting it on will also help to keep lips colourful longer.

There are a lucky few who are blessed with perfect lip proportions – fairly generous size, slightly turned up at the corners, a rounded cupid's bow and uniform size of top and bottom lips. If, on the other hand, your lip shape is not quite perfect, don't worry, there are very simple ways to fake the right shape. For lips that are too wide, you simply make a false

shape within the natural line of your lips. Cover the edges of your mouth with foundation, then using a lip brush, draw an outline that ends before it reaches the corners. Fill in the fake outline with the same colour. Slimline lips need a little more disguise. Many feel that application of colour outside the natural lip line is a good idea, but in practice this can result in smudging. Instead, outline

the natural shape with a pale shade and fill in with a slightly darker but toning lipstick colour. Avoid bright shades as these will only help to emphasise the thin shape. Although very attractive to some, many feel that full generous lips are not their cup of tea. Slim down by simply outlining with a deep shade of lip pencil just inside the natural line and fill in with your chosen lipstick, avoiding very pale or very bright colours. If your problem is badly matched lips, i.e. full bottom lip, thin top lip, you'll need two lipsticks in toning light and dark shades. Emphasise the smaller lip by applying pale foundation around its natural outline and then, using the paler shade

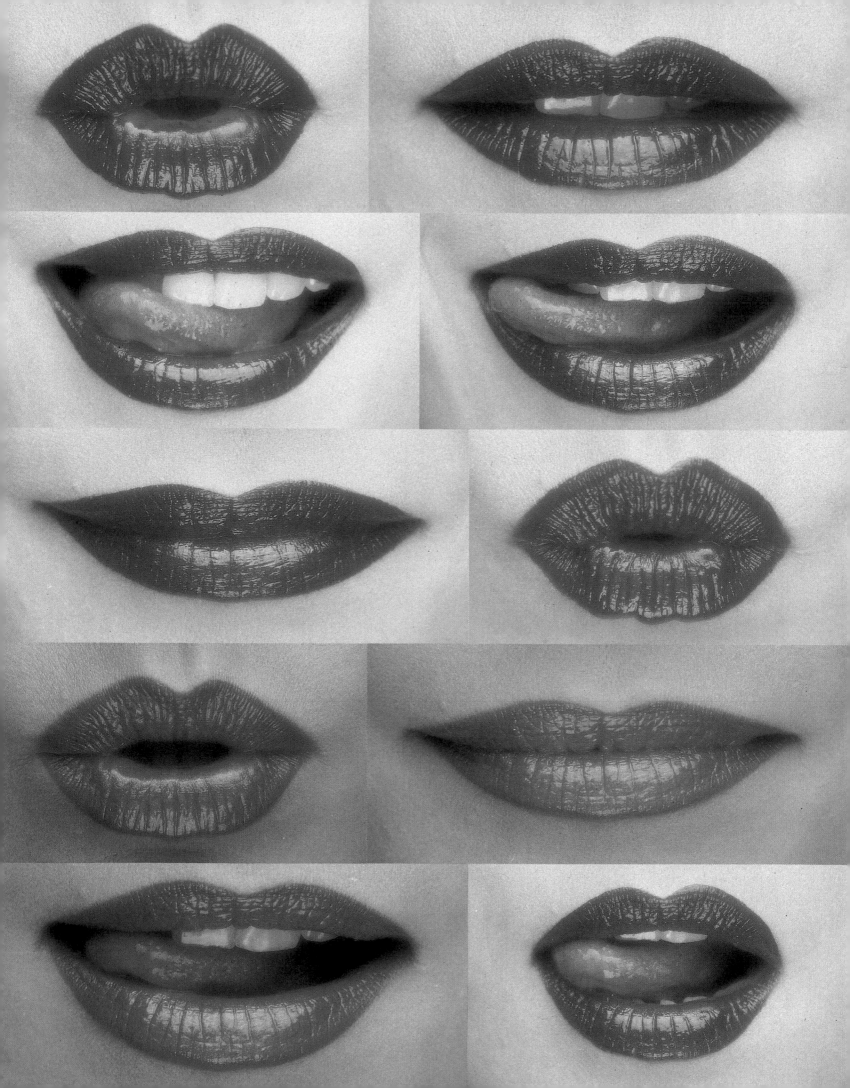

With confidence you can create many different moods.

paint the lip following the natural outline. Colour the fuller lip inside the natural line with the deeper shade. To finish the illusion blend a little of the paler shade on the centre where the two lips meet so that the difference between the shades you've used won't be noticeable.

Eyes Right

Learning the art of eye disguise is quite simple but probably the most important technique that you ever have to learn. Your eyes, apart from being the only visible 'living' part of your body, are your most important asset. Even if you have the most beautiful figure, or the longest legs, it's a known fact that anyone

meeting you will look you in the eyes first.

It matters not whether your eyes are big, small, deep set or protruding, eye make-up will help to compensate for all problems. The same principles that have applied for face and lip shaping work well on eyes too – light colours bring out and deep shades give shape and dimension.

1: *Here we see Susie. She has small, slightly uptilting eyes with a good basic shape and rich colour – without makeup they are just a nice pair of slightly unremarkable eyes.*

2: *This attempt at making up has failed miserably. In trying to emphasise their shape, she has drawn harsh black lines with a kohl pencil and dabbed on a nondescript pale blue shadow. The effect is to make her eyes look smaller and too strongly slanted.*

3: *Clever shading creates a dramatic and prominent eye shape. Pale pink shadow applied at inner corners gives extra width and this is smoothed just under the brow line to add shape. All the rest of the*

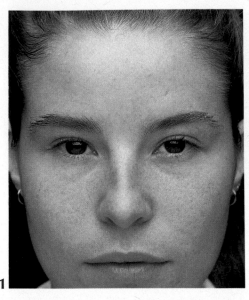

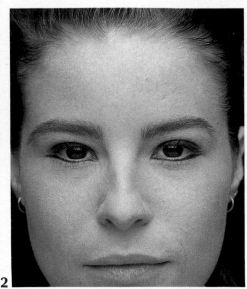

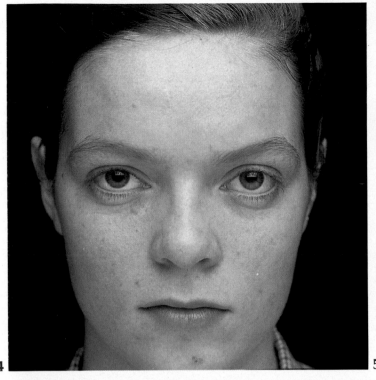

4

5

6

shading is achieved with a black kohl pencil. A line is drawn all around each eye and taken straight out at each corner instead of upwards to hide the slant. Using a good eyeshadow brush, the line is feathered to create the shading effect. To give extra dimension, white eye crayon has been drawn along the inner rim of lower lids before mascara was applied –

this gives an instant wide effect.

4: Here we see a perfect example of prominent, wide-set eyes; eyes that are just crying out to be made up and enhanced.

5: Light shadow at inner corners of eyes spaces them too far apart and the winged eyeliner just does nothing to shape,

succeeding in making the look very dated.

6: See how the use of a deep sable shadow gives drama and creates a wonderfully sultry effect. A rich copper shadow brushed right up to the nose immediately brings those wide-set eyes closer together and gives better proportion.

Chapter 4
Young Looks

The teens and early twenties are really the most exciting time for making up, especially now, when fashion-wise literally anything goes. And, whatever you do, providing you do it with style, you can get away with it, Some of the more way-out looks can, it must be said, look downright ugly but many can look very spectacular and history always shows that this is the age of experimentation.

1

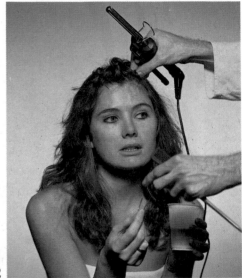

2

1: Debbie came into our photographic studio, a fresh faced girl just starting life as a model and ready to be transformed. We selected her because she has all the potential of a pretty girl who could be quite easily turned into a stunner.

2: Her softly permed hair is twisted in small sections and pinned to give more curl and bounce.

3: Debbie has a problem – too many late nights have given her black bags under her eyes. A pale cover stick is painted over the area and blended.

3

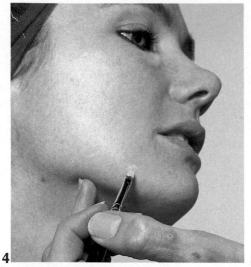

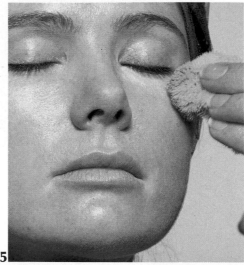

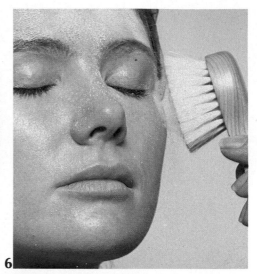

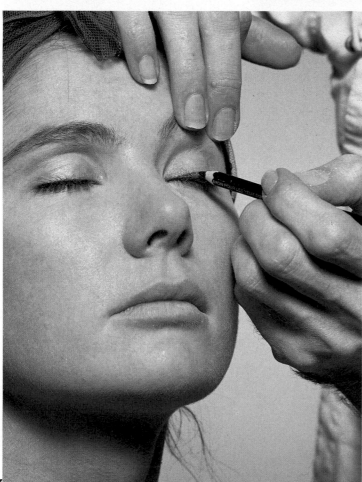

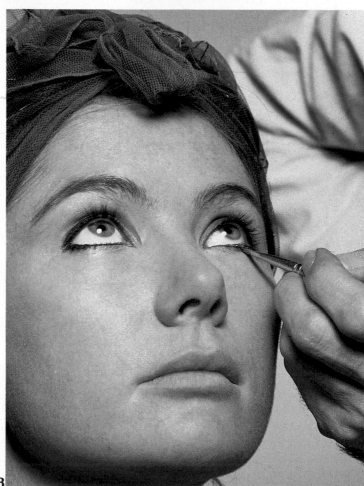

4: *There's no avoiding the odd spot – this one is quickly hidden with cover stick too.*

5: *A light, lotion foundation is gently patted with a cosmetic sponge all over the face to even colouring.*

6: *Translucent powder is applied liberally all over with cotton wool and the excess brushed away with a complexion brush.*

7: *Soft kohl pencil outlines Debbie's almond shape eyes.*

8: *The kohl line is softened with a brush.*

9: *Deep pink pressed powder shadow is applied to the upper lid and blended with a deep purple applied at outer corners and above the crease line.*

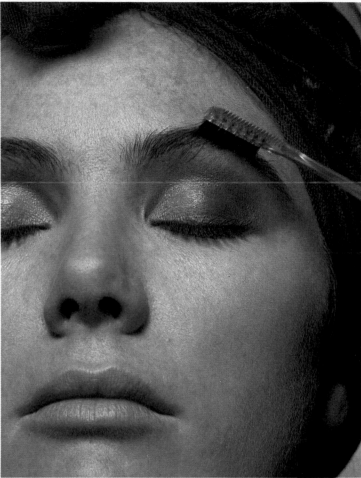

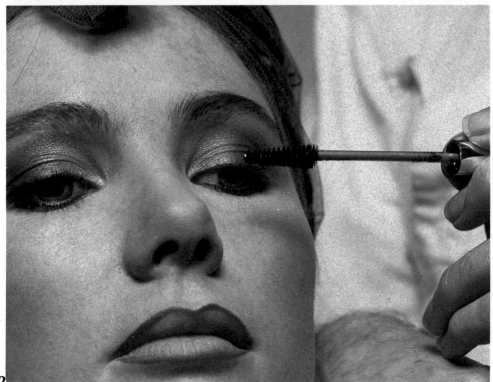

10: *A pale, frosted pink is brushed just under the brow line to emphasise the eye shape.*

11: *Debbie's eyebrows are quite dark and free of straggly hairs so they are just simply brushed into shape – no pencilling is necessary.*

12: *Eyes are given the final touch with two coats of brownish-black mascara.*

13: *A soft pink blusher co-ordinates with Debbie's eye shades. It's brushed just under the cheek bone and out towards the temples.*

As in all things it's a good idea to remember the old adage, 'don't run before you can walk'. In other words, learn the basics first and then you'll be much more expert at attempting the unusual. Start by perfecting a natural look that enhances your good points, then try out some more fun ideas when you know yourself and the techniques much better.

Answering the question 'When should I start to use make-up?' is rather like trying to answer 'How long is a piece of string?' because opinion varies. The only way I can give any kind of answer is to say that there's a time and a place for everything. Heavy black eyes and bright pink lips certainly look pretty silly at school but lovely in a disco. Similarly blusher and powder look fairly ridiculous on a day out in the country but perfectly suitable for a job in a bank. Sometimes it's a bitter pill to swallow, but you really should learn to be adaptable and create the right look for the right time.

14

15

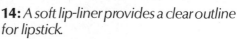

14: *A soft lip-liner provides a clear outline for lipstick.*

15: *Vivid pink lipstick put on with a brush will last longer.*

16: *The finished effect shows just how make-up has emphasised Debbie's beautiful assets. Eyes have more shape from the clever use of kohl and the upward sweep of shadow. Her lovely high cheek bones are more visible now with blusher brushed underneath.*

1: Jo, just like many teenagers loves trying out new fashion and make-up ideas and spent many happy hours in our studio with a hairdresser and make-up artist discussing cosmetic possibilities. Here, her face is clean and ready to start work. Too much partying has left her with very bad black shadows under her well shaped green eyes and she had a few spots on her chin too. Both problems were quickly hidden under a painting of cover stick and a light application of cream foundation.

2: Looking every inch a girl about to go to her first dance, we gave full emphasis to Jo's eyes for this look. Pale plum shadow is brushed all over top lids following a curving line from outer corners up to the brow. Navy blue kohl pencil outlines the shape and is brushed outwards to blend naturally into the plum shade. A little pale, frosted blue is added at inner corners to define the line. Here you can see clearly how contrasting colours succeed in making her eyes appear even greener than they naturally are. Blusher and lipstick are deliberately neutral in order not to detract attention from the eyes.

3: Shades of apricot and gold give Jo a real cover-girl look, yet this make-up is simplicity itself. Using just one colour shadow in a deep apricot shade, the shape of Jo's eyes is brought out by delicately shading with a frosted brown shadow crayon. Note, too, how the shadow is taken right up to the bridge of her nose to reduce the flattened effect. Gold glitter is painted over the whole upper lid area for the extra sparkle. Burnt orange-gold lips echo the complete gilded effect.

Overleaf: A pre-Raphaelite hairdo and stunning colours turn Jo into a budding pop star in a matter of minutes. Deep cerise shadow teamed with frosted aqua and navy liner would normally clash horribly; here they create a truly dramatic effect. Blusher and lips in toning vibrant pink add to a look that is certainly not for the shy or faint-hearted and perfect for the extrovert.

1: *Ling Tai is an extremely pretty young Chinese girl with a very classic face. If you analyse her features you will find that she has a round face shape, a broad, slightly flat nose, characteristically small, almond shape eyes and full lips.*

1

2

3

2: *This attempt at making up has made some classic mistakes. Her foundation is far too pale, her brows overdrawn. Sparkling blue shadow follows and emphasises the eye shape and the heavy black line literally closes them up. Her pink blusher certainly shapes her face and matches the cyclamen coloured lipstick but just creates the feeling that Ling is an over-painted doll.*

3: *Now, see how a pretty girl can be turned into a beautiful one. A toning foundation has softened her look instantly. Just look at those eyes too. Peach frosted shadow has been applied all over lids, and charcoal grey painted at inner corners gives shape to the bridge of her nose. The same charcoal brushed under lower lids and out at the sides gives extra width. Soft amber blusher creates a more* sculptured effect and is also used to help shape her nose, by dusting a little down each side. A warm, ginger-tone, glossy lipstick brings out the natural roundness of her lips.

1

1: *This lovely, classic English Rose keeps her look simple for daytime. Natural shades of peach and soft rose for lips and cheeks and a light smudging of dark brown kohl pencil to accentuate her eyes*

create a perfect, soft and young look.

2: *Classic features need little make-up change for a glamour evening look. A light, soft pink highlighter gives extra*

dimension to the eyes. Lip colour is strengthened and a slick of gloss is added. Clever accessorising with a headband made from twisted ribbon and material scraps give her extra nighttime style.

2

2

3

1: *Eye shades of khaki and pewter blend perfectly with this stunning evening dress. Amber blusher and pale toffee coloured lips tone with this beautifully co-ordinated look.*

2: *Identical twins, identically made-up with a look to turn most heads in their direction.*

3: *See how a make-up change can make identical twins look completely different? Here's an example of day and night looks for lookalike people.*

4: *A fantasy of twisted scarves frames a dramatic make-up. Foundation is kept deliberately light coloured to accentuate those stunning eyes.*

4

1

1: *Light foundation, brilliant pink blusher and shades of blue and lilac for eyes add up to a make-up that perfectly complements an outrageous hairstyle.*

2: *Deep emerald shadow is skilfully brushed under the lids and round the eyes to highlight their rich hazel tones. Black liner softly frames the shape. Deep olive skin is shaped and shaded with rich, bronze blusher and toning lips.*

3: *Soft lips and cheeks leave the emphasis on strong eye make-up. Shades of rich, deep, royal blue blend into soft sky blue to echo the same colour accessories.*

4: *Stunning green eyes are given more prominence with a blend of bronze and copper shadows, rich burnt-orange lips and deliberately pale complexion.*

5: *A look that says 'fresh, young and healthy.' This girl's completely in the pink. Notice how everything about this make-up is soft save for the rather strong eyeliner shape? This look is reminiscent of the '50s' but right up to the minute for today's fashion trends.*

Chapter 5
Ten Years On

The years between early twenties and mid-thirties are an interesting time. Gone is the need to constantly experiment and many women tend to start to get into a rut make-up-wise. This should never really happen because it's just as important now as it always will be.

It's a sad fact, but true, that the ageing process really starts to get going even as early as the age of twenty-one or so. Of

1: *When Aimee walked into the studio, she was just a face in the crowd. With hair scraped away from a completely bare face she was pretty but hardly noticeable.*
2: *No, it is not a famous American pop singer, this is Aimee again, totally transformed. The full hairstyle accentuates her good bone structure and this is further helped by applying blusher right up to the temples. Suddenly, too, a pair of unremarkable eyes positively smoulder with clever shading and shaping.*

course this does vary from person to person but, from here on in it's a wise lady who pays extra special attention to skin care. As you get older, your skin starts to get dryer and elastin, the constituent that gives it it's ability to spring back, starts to cease its function. By your mid-thirties it's stopped working altogether so nothing short of plastic surgery will rid you of wrinkles. Far better to avoid them with regular moisturising; this will also give your skin vital protection against the elements.

It's doubtful that you will notice any changes overnight, but gradually, you may become aware that your skin doesn't have its usual suppleness. This signals the time for you to try new preparations: a slightly richer moisturiser, a cream foundation in favour of a lotion, cream or automatic eye shadows instead of loose powder and so on.

By now you will have a very good idea of the ideal shape you should be painting on your face and daily make-up will be much faster and simpler. If this is

1: *Fiona has the perfect canvas for make-up although when we found her she was sporting a completely scrubbed complexion – a pity because she really needs to even up high colouring and accentuate her eyes.*

2: *As Fiona is really happiest with little or no make-up we devised this totally natural look for her that takes just a few minutes to copy. Pink colouring on cheeks disappears under green cover cream and a creamy beige foundation, brown kohl pencil gives shape at outer corners of eyes and mascara lengthens and beautifies her lashes. A soft peach blusher creates a healthy glow and soft coral lipstick keeps the look completely fresh and natural.*

3: *A dramatic evening blouse needs a* **1**

more theatrical look. Eyes are shaped with pale terracotta and frosted peach and shaded with brown kohl pencil. Soft amber blusher gives extra definition and a very pale frosted lipstick, outlined in deep pink, gives extra shape and excitement.

4: *This make-up takes the transformation of Fiona one stage further, giving her an extra special polish with a look that wouldn't be out of place in the pages of a magazine. Burnt copper shimmer shadow highlights under the brow line. A rich deep blue shadow is brushed just above the crease line and under lower lids with a soft gold highlighting upper lids at the centre to give eyes an extra sparkle. Because her eyes have a much stronger look, Fiona's lips are painted in a dramatic burnt orange with blusher strengthened too to complete the effect.*

2

3

4

the case, then you're an ideal candidate for falling into that rut, producing the same old face and colours every day.

A great way to avoid this little pitfall is to open your cosmetic drawer, arm yourself with cleansing lotion and tissues and shut the door on the world for an hour or so while you try out some colours and shapes to transform yourself once again. Most cosmetics will last for quite a long time and it's very rare that anyone actually uses up any eye shadow, blusher or lipstick completely and doesn't have a store of half used products lying around somewhere, ready for just this eventuality.

1

2

1: *Lesley is a good looking young housewife who tends to use lack of time as a reason for her clean, scrubbed look. She's blessed with stunning turquoise eyes, a clear complexion and beautiful, flowing blond hair.*

2: *This daytime look has been kept deliberately soft and very simple. A blend of khaki and beige shapes her eyes, bringing out their natural colour and soft coral blusher and lipstick give gentle emphasis.*

3: *This look graphically shows how easy it is to obtain a totally dated and very wrong look with cosmetics. False lashes, unless your natural ones are very short indeed, look positively 1950's. Blusher and highlighter have been applied in ugly, straight lines with no thought paid to careful blending and crimson lips are far too bright and harsh for a blonde.*

4: *Lesley wanted to try out a slightly different idea for an evening make-up.*

Here, blusher has been used not only to shape but also in place of eye shadow. A pale frosted brown has been used at outer corners to give eyes dimension and very fine false lashes add a touch of glamour. Lip colour for night time is stronger and tones beautifully with the overall pink effect of this make-up.

3

4

1: *Catherine has a problem shared by many dark skinned people – uneven skin pigmentation. This is clearly visible here – she has light patches on cheeks, dark areas around her eyes and characteristic brown spots on her nose.*

2: *Here, her make-up, although expertly applied, emphasises the uneven colouring and makes her eyes seem heavier and slightly hooded.*

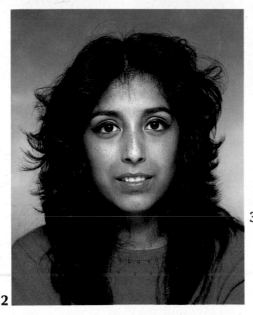

3: *A shade of cake foundation a touch lighter than her darkest tones and a shade darker than her lightest tones provides an ideal covering base for a more subtle make-up.*

With Catherine's deep skin colouring, she can afford to be adventurous with her choice of eye shades: this brilliant combination of iridescent blue and mauve looks stunning. Because she has such prominent eyes, liquid liner can draw a defined line without looking harsh and unnatural. Blusher is applied high on cheek bones to further underline the importance of the eye make-up.

4: *Dark skinned girls can wear pink and blue for a striking effect. Here rich frosted shades of midnight blue and petrol create beautiful eyes. Lip, cheek and nail colours co-ordinate perfectly to add to an exciting outdoors look.*

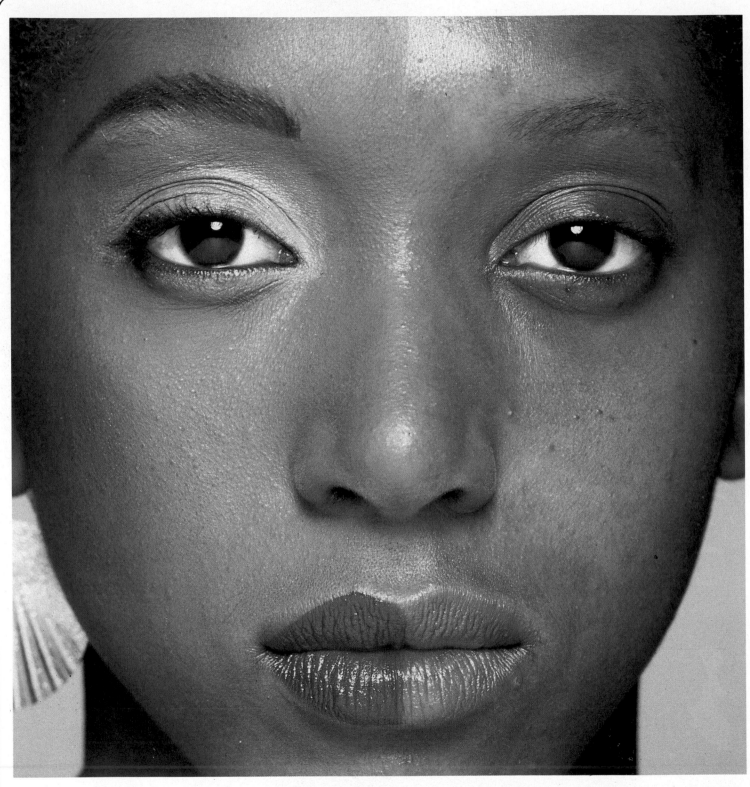

No, this isn't the latest in punk make-up! It's our way of showing very graphically how make-up has worked to bring out the best and hide the problems. Note how foundation has obliterated minor blemishes, dark down on upper lip and over-shiny skin. Blusher slims down chubby cheeks, lipstick hides uneven lip colouring, eyebrow pencil creates a frame for shimmering eye shades.

The finished look demonstrates how black girls can happily get away with really strong eye colour. Notice too how blusher is carried round the eye and up to the temples? With this stark hairdo this trick slims and frames the face perfectly.

1: *A very understated make-up creates a 'poor little rich girl' look. With hair casually brushed away from the face, careful attention has been paid to shape with light shading in shades of pink.*

2: *If you've got beautiful shaped lips then flaunt them. Strawberry blonde hair, coupled with yellow and amber accessories, dictate toning face shades made dramatic with brilliant orange lips.*

3: *A soft and simple daytime make-up is made instantly into an evening look with rich toffee shaded lips, carefully outlined to improve their shape.*

1

4: *Not every girl can be as adventurous as this. Golden shadow highlights under the brow line and a combination of copper and brown kohl shape the eyes. Classic high cheek bones are sculptured with pale golden frosted highlighter and rich peach shader. Soft, golden coral glossy lips add the perfect finishing touch.*

2

3

1: *Softly tanned skins on a warm summer evening need little to add a touch of beauty. Eyes are simply shaded and shaped with black kohl pencil, shine is toned down with translucent powder* and lips are given a touch of colour with brilliant pink.

2: *Use of colour has been deliberately played down here with shades to tone* with an olive complexion. Eyes are emphasised with shadows blending from black through to pale silver. Smoky pink lips complete a totally co-ordinated look.

Summer tanned skin needs very little or no make-up at all especially when you're young. Over the next two pages you'll find a montage of photographs of the same girl enjoying the sunshine with little more than a wardrobe ot glossy lipsticks, kohl pencil and waterproof mascara. The looks are stunning, fresh and wholesome but could be ruined by strap marks, and burnt patches. Her most important holiday accessory therefore is her sunscreen that ensures even, light tanning without pain.

Chapter 6
Maturing Gracefully

Just because the age of forty has gone by it doesn't mean that you're over the hill. Far from it. In fact the mature woman is very much in fashion.

You have only to look as far as the film industry to see just how popular the forty-pluses are. Jane Fonda, Sophia Loren, Brigitte Bardot and even our own Joan Collins are all enjoying more success now that they have seen the last of their thirties. Perhaps one of the reasons for this is that maturity tends to bring a more relaxed outlook. Life isn't quite so frantic and fraught because age brings an ability to be more philosophical and you're less likely to let major problems upset you as much as fifteen years ago. Many women are fast discovering that this calmer attitude to life makes it a happier and more fulfilling time than any other age group.

1: *Alison, a bright, happy lady, agreed to let us photograph her without make-up to show graphically how lack of cosmetics can add years to a face. Her fine complexion is now marred by broken veins and laughter lines are emphasised without camouflage.*

1

2: *After applying green colour corrector, a base of warm beige gives subtle colour without looking unnatural. A soft turquoise cream shadow – which suits dry skin – follows the shape of her eye and only a single coat of mascara is needed to enhance lashes. Soft apricot lips and toning blusher give colour without looking harsh. The finished result takes at least ten years away from Alison's age, without looking like mutton done up as lamb, and it should take no more than six minutes to complete.*

3: *For a fast change into an evening look, blush and lip shades remain the same. To give an extra touch of glamour, Alison has chosen a frosted sable shade blended with her blusher to shape her eyes. Note too that she has cleverly hidden characteristic neck wrinkles with a pretty pearl choker.*

2

3

Now, just because the children have grown up and flown the nest there are no excuses for sitting back and becoming a frump. Instead it is time to adapt your beauty routine, complement the advance of time and make the most of it.

Basic skin care is of the utmost importance now, even if you have always been blessed with a trouble free complexion, it's almost certainly starting to get very dry indeed.

Fast losing the suppleness of youth, it will desperately need daily and nightly moisturising with rich lotions or creams to help redress the balance. Another danger area is eyelids which could show a tendency to become crepey, making shadow application more difficult. Use of a good eye cream does help to reduce the risk of this happening in the first place but avoiding the use of bright colours will help reduce its visibility too. In fact, subtlety is the watchword for make-up now. Soft, muted colours are far more flattering and far less ageing.

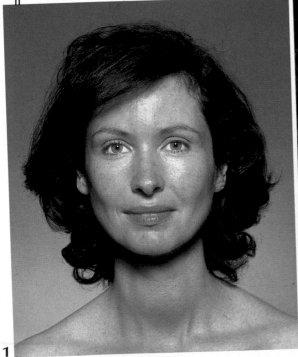

1

2

1: *Slim and attractive with lovely dark auburn hair and green eyes, Annabella has the potential to be a very elegant and good looking lady.*

2: *For her daytime look we chose soft and subtle shades of pink to suit her*

English Rose looks. Eyes are emphasised with a line of soft brown kohl pencil and delicately shadowed with a matte pale orchid. Rose pink blusher and lips colour blend beautifully.

3: *For a quick five minute change to an evening look, we kept the same basic*

make-up. Dark brown pencil is added for strength and silver grey shadow is brushed over lids and winged upwards. Blusher in the same shade as before is strengthened and lips are given a coat of a richer pink with a slick of gloss on top.

1: *Iris, seen here without her make-up, has beautiful blue eyes and a very good bone structure. She really should wear make-up to hide those broken veins and take away a few years.*

2: *This make-up achieves nothing. Bright blue shadow and strong dark lines look* positively hard and ugly. A light covering of powder does nothing to disguise those broken veins and dark red lipstick is far too harsh for Iris's colouring.

3: *Iris now looks ten years younger with this softer make-up. Pearly grey shadow and brown pencil really bring out the* colour of her eyes. Uneven colouring is hidden under green cover cream and a warm beige foundation. A peach blusher gives warmth and pinky-beige lipstick completes the softening effect.

1: *We met Sharron (left) spending a happy Mediterranean holiday with her family. It may be hard to believe but Sharman (right) is her fourteen year old daughter!*

Sharron is a very pretty lady who, like many with fair complexions, tends to redden a little in the sun. Had we met her before, we would have suggested a higher protection sunscreen on her face in order to avoid this happening. Instead, we designed this informal, easy to copy natural holiday make-up.

2: *A deep golden beige foundation gives a soft glow to sunburnt skin. Eyes are simply enhanced with dark charcoal grey kohl pencil drawn all around and brushed upwards at outer corners. Liberal application of brownish black waterproof mascara is guaranteed to stay put even on the hottest of nights. Amber blusher, lightly applied under cheek bones and soft rose lips completed Sharron's soft, young, summer evening make-up.*

Below *Eve is one of those rare and lucky women who can really look good without a stitch of make-up. She has a lovely, fresh complexion, sparkling eyes and a dazzling smile and very pretty elfin-like face. Here she is sporting just the very barest of essentials in natural toning shades.*

1: *Here's a perfect example of make-up co-ordinating with an outfit – every colour in Eve's evening blouse is mirrored in her face. Charcoal shadow on her eyes is covered with beautiful gold glitter and a yellow-gold powder shadow is used with dramatic effect as highlighter on cheek bones and at temples. Brilliant pink blusher isn't just reserved for cheeks either, it's used to give more emphasis to Eve's smooth and wrinkle-free forehead. Deep peach lipstick is just a perfect match to her blouse.*

2: *For an alternative glamorous evening, a soft khaki shadow blends perfectly into a rosy blusher which is swept from the eyelids up to her temples. The complete effect of this make-up gives Eve real style.*

1

2

Chapter 7
A Time and a Place?

Having by now learnt all the tricks of the trade make-up-wise, now is the time to start having fun and branching out. Because, once the art of disguise, enhancement, blending and colour choice are known there is no end to the number of ways that you can ring the changes.

For special parties, the changing seasons, new outfits, new job or even just to cheer you up there is nothing better than a new make-up to give confidence and add a bit of spice to life in general.

Head for the Sun
This is the era of health, fitness and the great outdoors. Those of us who are not entering Marathons are either jogging,

swimming, dancing or taking part in some kind of sport or other to keep in trim.

The real sporty look is natural, fresh and clear skinned. The barest minimum of make-up should be applied and, to allow the skin to rest and breathe, it's best to stick to just a little eye make-up, perhaps a dot of cream blusher and natural lips. This is when waterproof cosmetics become invaluable so that no matter how hot and sticky you get, you can always be sure of looking your best. Look for automatic eyeshadows and waterproof mascara that will stay put no matter what and, if you're out in the sun, buy a lipstick that contains a sunscreen to protect your lips too.

A Time and a Place?

Seasonal Changes

Just as you climb out of your winter woollies at the first warm breath of spring, so too should you switch your make-up. This should not just suit your outfit but also the light – cold, grey winter days demand a heavier make-up, whereas lighter, brighter spring and summer days dictate a far more natural look.

1 and 2: *Honey-tanned skin needs little or no make-up. Soft bronze blusher to shape, perhaps a rich deep red lipstick or just lip gloss and a soft pencil outline round the eyes for extra sparkle.*

2

3: *As summer tans fade and days become grey and miserable, put some warmth into your make-up with rich shades of burgundy and copper.*

4: *Winter heralds the start of the party season and a chance to wear glamorous glittery outfits and create an exciting new look with heavy eyes, pale and interesting complexion and startling lip shades.*

3

4

1

Same girl but two completely different looks for very special occasions.

1: Here brilliant shades of green and gold cleverly echo the shades in Debra's choker necklace.

2: This stunning evening blouse needs a spectacular make-up to complement it.

Eyes are shaped with silver and charcoal and given extra dimension with pink blusher applied under the brow line and right up to her nose to slim and shape. Lips are painted a pale candy pink in order to leave full emphasis on the eyes.

Fantasy Faces *Fancy dress parties can often give you the ideal excuse for creating your own unique fantasy face. In fact, you can save yourself quite a bit of money by making your face the actual fancy dress.*

1: Just a Pussycat *A mane of strawberry blonde hair coupled with a fox scarf can make you the most glamorous lion at the party. This incredible make-up was drawn with charcoal and black and white eyepencils. It took over an hour to do but it's a real work of art.*

3

3: Pure Fantasy *This beautiful look is entitled 'Midsummer Nights Dream'. A soft ivory foundation forms the base, charcoal pencil provides the outline and pink and lilac pressed powder shadow create the subtle shading.*

5: Be a witch *This stunning creation instantly turns you into a rather beautiful witch: team it with a long black dress and a broomstick and there you are ready to bewitch all at the party.*

5

FEATURING THE PHOTOGRAPHY OF PETER BARRY
This edition published 1983 by Book Club Associates.
First published in Great Britain by Colour Library Books Ltd.
© 1983 Illustrations and Text: Colour Library Books Ltd.,
    Guildford, Surrey, England.
Colour separations by LLOVET S.A. Barcelona, Spain.
Display and text filmsetting by ACESETTERS LTD., Richmond, Surrey, England.
Printed and bound in Barcelona, Spain by CAYFOSA and EUROBINDER.
All rights reserved
ISBN 0-86283-107-5
COLOUR LIBRARY BOOKS